MW00534348

BRUSH YOUR TEETH!

BRUSH YOUR TEETH!

BRANDON'S SONG FOR HEALTHY TEETH

BRUSH YOUR TEETH!

BRUSH YOUR TEETH!

BRANDON'S SONG FOR HEALTHY TEETH

Skylight Books
An Imprint of Tandem Light Press

Written by D.M. Whitaker
Illustrated by Ambadi Kumar

SkyLight Books

An imprint of Tandem Light Press

950 Herrington Road

Suite C128

Lawrenceville, GA 30044

Copyright © 2020

Tandem Light Press paperback edition November 2020

ISBN: 978-1-7353210-0-4

Library of Congress Control Number: 2019952807

PRINTED IN THE UNITED STATES OF AMERICA

I would like to thank my husband, Brandon, for beliving in me and encouraging me to leap with BIG faith. To my sister, Da'Keisha, thank you for being a second set of eyes and ears and cheerleader throughout this project. Most importantly, all thanks to God for planting the seed and opening the doors.

To my big boy Duce, who finds joy in the smallest, yet most meaningful experiences.

- "Kweeeee-Shaaaa"

"It's time to brush your teeth!"
Mommy and Daddy say.

BRUSH YOUR TEETH
BRUSH YOUR TEETH
123

BRUSH YOUR TEETH
BRUSH YOUR TEETH
ABC

BRUSH YOUR TEETH
BRUSH YOUR TEETH

TOP AND BOTTOM,
ABC

BRUSH YOUR TEETH
BRUSH YOUR TEETH
123

TOP AND BOTTOM
SIDE TO SIDE
BRUSH THEM RIGHT

TOP AND BOTTOM
SIDE TO SIDE
BRUSH THEM RIGHT

TOP AND BOTTOM
SIDE TO SIDE

BRUSH YOUR TEETH
DAY AND NIGHT

BRUSH YOUR TEETH
BRUSH YOUR TEETH
123

"All done!" Brandon says.

"Great job brushing, Brandon!" Mommy says.

"Oh, what a day! We played with friends, read books, and colored. We ate great treats and had a big supper," Daddy says.

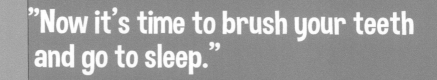

"Now it's time to brush your teeth and go to sleep."

"Brush your teeth! Brush your teeth!" Brandon says.

BRUSH YOUR TEETH
BRUSH YOUR TEETH
123

BRUSH YOUR TEETH
BRUSH YOUR TEETH
ABC

BRUSH YOUR TEETH
BRUSH YOUR TEETH

TOP AND BOTTOM,
ABC

BRUSH YOUR TEETH
BRUSH YOUR TEETH
123

TOP AND BOTTOM
SIDE TO SIDE
BRUSH THEM RIGHT

TOP AND BOTTOM
SIDE TO SIDE
BRUSH THEM RIGHT

TOP AND BOTTOM
SIDE TO SIDE

BRUSH YOUR TEETH
DAY AND NIGHT

BRUSH YOUR TEETH
BRUSH YOUR TEETH
123

"All done!" Brandon says.

"Great job brushing your teeth, Big Boy!" Daddy says.

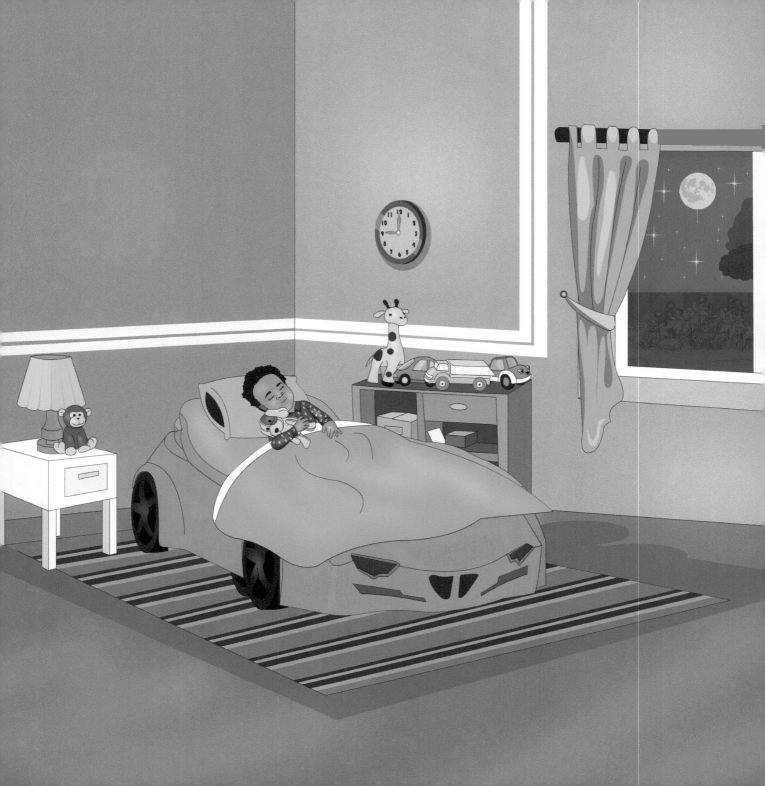

"Good night, Brandon!"
Mommy and Daddy say.

BRUSH YOUR TEETH! BRUSH YOUR TEETH!

in B major
Lyrics by D.M. Whitaker

BRUSH YOUR TEETH! BRUSH YOUR TEETH!

in C major
Lyrics by D.M. Whitaker

ABOUT THE AUTHOR

D.M. WHITAKER was born in Omaha, Nebraska to a mom and dad that loved reading books to her and her siblings. Thus, her love for reading and sharing those same traditions with her dear sons have been valuable and intricate in their development.

Inspired by being a mother and educator, D.M. loves to write children's books and rhymes that will sketch beautiful memories in children's hearts and inspire them to be their best every day. D.M. Whitaker currently resides in San Antonio, Texas, with her husband Brandon and dear sons, Brandon, II, affectionally known as "Duce" and Elisha. She enjoys being a wife, mother, author, blogger, and momprenuer.

CPSIA information can be obtained
at www.ICGtesting.com
Printed in the USA
BVHW020503250720
584536BV00017B/340